The Best of

Panchatantra

Compiled by Mrs Rungeen Singh

Young Learner Publications™

G-1, Rattan Jyoti,
18, Rajendra Place
New Delhi-110008 (INDIA)
Ph.: 25750801, 25820556
Fax : 91-11-25764396

Printed at : Kumar Offset Printers, Delhi-110092

CONTENTS

THE SINGING DONKEY

A donkey started working for a washerman. He carried the clothes to be washed by the washerman. From the hut he went to the river, where the washerman washed the clothes, and then he came back with the washed clothes loaded on his back. He was quite happy with his easy job.

The donkey was happy, but one thing still made him sad. The old washerman did not give the donkey enough to eat, so he used to feel very hungry all the time.

One day, the donkey happened to stray to some big fields nearby. There were many crops growing in those fields. So he started going there every day to eat the crops, when no one was watching him.

Now he felt nice because he got enough to eat and no longer went hungry. One day, he was eating the crops in the fields, when suddenly, he felt as if someone was watching him.

He felt someone was hiding behind a tree. He became afraid that he would be caught and punished.

He stopped eating and stood still for a while, straining his ears. Yes, there was someone there. He slowly moved to see who it was.

It was a fox. The donkey looked at the fox thinking that he might hurt him. But the fox smiled and began to talk with the donkey. The fox looked very friendly.

Panchatantra

Soon the donkey and the fox became friends. They would also eat the crops in the fields together.

Now the donkey was really happy. He had a good friend, good food to eat and an easy job as well. Life was good.

One night, the fox and the donkey met again. That day, they saw big watermelons in another field and both started eating them.

The watermelons were so sweet that the donkey loved to eat them.

He told the fox, "I am feeling so happy, that I want to sing."

The fox said, "No, dear donkey. Don't sing. If you sing, the man who looks after these fields will hear you. He will find out that we are eating his crops. Then we will be punished."

The donkey said. "You are needlessly afraid. Nothing will happen. Singing makes me happy, and so I will sing."

The fox said, "The owner of this field is sleeping close by. If he hears you sing, he will beat us and we will never be able to eat this delicious crop again."

But the donkey would not listen. He had made up his mind to sing. The fox then said, "All right, sing if you have to, but stay quiet just now. You may sing after two minutes. Let me go first."

In a flash of a second, the fox had jumped over the fence and hid himself. Then the donkey started singing.

Panchatantra

He lifted his head and let out a loud, 'hee-haw', 'hee-haw.' He thought he was singing, but the clever fox knew that he was just braying. The donkey sang louder, enjoying himself. Now the owner of the field woke up.

The man looked around and saw the donkey braying. He also saw how much crop had been eaten up.

He thought that the donkey alone had eaten up everything because he could not see anyone else.

The man became very angry. He picked up a stick and ran towards the donkey. But the donkey did not see him because he was busy singing.

The man hit the donkey with the stick. He hit him so hard that soon the donkey forgot to sing and started crying.

The man then threw the stick and went away. The donkey was afraid that he might come back and beat him again.

So slowly the donkey joined the fox in the next field, and lay down on the ground because his body was hurting all over.

The fox said, "I am sorry that the man beat you so much, but I told you not to sing. Now because of you, we cannot eat in the fields. Life had been so good. Why did you have to sing?"

"Yes, I have been very foolish. I did not listen to you. I am really sorry, dear fox," replied the donkey sadly.

A flock of pigeons always flew together like a family. They would start in the morning to gather food. The wise king of the pigeons would lead them all.

Once they had been flying in search of food for a long time but failed to find anything.

Suddenly, the king of the pigeons looked down and saw some rice grains on the ground. The other pigeons saw them too and wanted to go down, but the king stopped them from flying downwards.

He said, "Wait. This is a forest. Rice does not grow in a forest. Something is wrong. We should not go down."

A young pigeon said, "I am very hungry. There is no one there to harm us. So, I am flying down for sure."

The youngest pigeon flew down. Then one of the older pigeons said, "The young ones don't think before they act. We should not go down, but we cannot leave him alone."

11

So all of them, except the king, flew down to be with the young pigeon. As soon as they sat down, they got caught in a net.

The net had been put there by a man. He had scattered grains of rice on the ground and spread a net over them. He had then hidden himself behind a tree.

Now the man saw the pigeons getting caught in the net. He was very happy because it was the first time that he had caught so many pigeons together.

He came out to catch all the pigeons. The king of the pigeons saw the man. He said, "Listen. You all must fly away from here or this man will kill you."

The youngest pigeon started crying. His mother scolded him, "When the king told you not to come down for the rice grains, why didn't you obey him? Now because of you, we all will soon be dead."

"Ma, I am sorry. Please don't leave me alone," cried the young pigeon.

"We never leave anyone alone. So don't worry," assured the mother pigeon.

The king said, "Listen. That man is coming here to catch you all. You cannot get out of the net. So, all of you will have to fly away together with the net."

The moment the king said, "Gootturgooo, one, two, three," all the pigeons, flapped their wings at the same time and flew up together, and the net went with them.

The man felt sad because he had lost not only all the pigeons, but also his net.

The pigeons flew higher and higher. Then a pigeon said, "Dear king, we are safe now, but how will we get out of this net ? We are still caught in it."

The wise king said, "Let us go to the king of mice. He will surely be able to help us. Just follow me."

A pigeon asked, "A mouse is so small. How can it help us get out of this big net?"

The king said, "The king mouse once helped a lion escape by gnawing the strong strings with his sharp teeth. He will certainly help us as he is my friend. Now wait for my signal to fly down together."

All the pigeons flew down together with their feet still caught up in the net. Then they sat down on the ground, near a big tree. In a hole in the ground, under the big tree, lived the king of mice.

The king mouse was sitting in his hole, looking outside. When he saw the pigeon king and others, he came out and asked, "What brings you here?"

The king pigeon said, "My friends are all caught in a net, laid by a man."

The king mouse said, "Oh! These men trouble us so much."

The king pigeon said, "I need your help. Please free them from the net."

The king mouse said, "Certainly. I will start at once. A true friend is one who helps in times of need."

The king mouse quickly gmawed away the strings of the net, and one by one the pigeons became free. Then the mouse carried the pieces of the net into his hole to use them for a soft bed. All the pigeons thanked the king mouse for helping them. They flew back home, glad to be free from the net.

There was once a kind and gentle elephant. He was friendly and never hurt anyone. So everyone loved him. The elephant would go to the temple every morning, and pass through a busy market.

There the florist would give the elephant a garland of yellow flowers every day, and the fruitseller would give him a fruit every day.

All the people would stand around the elephant and pat him lovingly and kindly, which the elephant greatly enjoyed.

When the elephant got so much love and kindness, he gave love and kindness to others too. He often took the small children of the shopkeepers for joy rides.

One day, the florist felt like teasing the elephant. When the elephant came, the florist put out his left hand with a garland. But he did not give the garland.

He had a needle in his right hand with which he used to make garlands.

He pricked the elephant's trunk with it. The elephant let out a loud cry, and the people around started laughing.

The elephant was in great pain where the needle had pricked him so he sat down to rest. He felt hurt and angry. Slowly, he got up and walked away quietly. He could still hear the florist and the people around laughing at him.

He did not go to the temple that day. He went straight to the pond nearby and filled his trunk with the dirty water of the pond. Then he walked to the shop of the florist.

When he reached the florist, the florist started laughing at the elephant again. Then the elephant aimed his trunk at the florist and sprayed the dirty water right onto the florist.

All the dirty water fell on the florist and in the shop. All the flowers of the shop were dirtied by the water, and that day the florist did not earn any money because nobody bought the dirty flowers.

The elephant went to the florist the next morning and stood outside his shop. The scared florist quietly gave him a garland of flowers for the temple.

The florist had learnt that it was best to be kind to the elephant because then the elephant too would be kind to him. But if anyone teased the elephant, then he would hit back. So he decided not to trouble the elephant at all.

A MATTER OF TRUST

A fox was very hungry. He saw a peacock sitting on the branch of a tree.

The fox wanted to eat the peacock, but knew that he could not climb the tree.

The clever fox said to the peacock, "Why are you sitting on the tree? Is it to save yourself from me ? But now I can't hurt you."

The peacock asked, "Why this sudden change of heart?"

The fox said, "I have to be good. It has been decided in a meeting that now animals cannot kill each other for food."

"Do you mean to say that lions and tigers will eat grass from today?" asked the peacock, laughing at the fox.

The fox had no answer but he could no longer wait to eat the peacock.

So the fox said to the peacock, "This is a very good point. Come down and we will go to the king to discuss this with him."

The peacock smiled and said, "We need not go to them. It is not necessary."

"Why not?" asked the fox.

"Because I can see your friends coming here," replied the clever peacock.

"Who are they?" asked the fox. The peacock knew that the fox was afraid of the hounds because the hounds could kill him.

The peacock said, "Some hounds are coming."

The fox got scared and turned to run away. Then the peacock laughed and said, "Why are you running away? You said no animal would kill each other."

The fox said, "Maybe the hounds have not heard of this meeting."

The peacock was glad that he had not trusted the fox because now it was clear that the fox had been telling lies.

THE WEAK CAN BE STRONG TOO!

Once, an earthquake shook a village so badly that all the people left the village to live elsewhere. A big group of mice started living in the village. The mice were very happy there.

But after a few days, a small herd of elephants started passing through that village. The herd would trample many mice to death under their huge feet.

This made the mice sad and they held a meeting.

In the meeting, the king mouse said, "I will go to the king elephant and ask him to change their route."

As decided, the king mouse went to the king elephant and said, "Oh, King Elephant. We are dying because of you all. Please change your route. Whenever you need us, we will help you."

The king elephant laughed and said, "You are so small. How can you help us? But don't worry, we will change our route so that you all remain safe."

The king mouse thanked the king elephant and ran away happily to tell the good news to all the other mice. All of them were overjoyed to hear the good news.

After some days, the king mouse heard the call of the king elephant. He felt that the elephants were in danger. The elephants had been caught in a net, and the next day, they would be taken to the king's camp to be used in the army.

The king mouse shouted to all the mice to come with him. They saw the elephants caught in a net.

The king mouse spoke loudly, "My dear mice! These elephants had changed their route for us. Now we must help them. Come on, let us bite off this net and let them free."

All the mice started gnawing at the strings of the net with their sharp teeth. They did not rest till the whole net was cut and the elephants were free.

The king elephant then said, "Thank you so much, dear friends."

The king mouse said, "Don't waste time, king elephant. Run away from here before the king's people come to catch you all. Don't worry. We will always remain friends helping each other."

The king elephant, said, "Thanks again. You all look so small and weak, but you all are really big and strong."

There was a tiger who had become very weak and old. It was no longer possible for him to hunt other animals. Thinking that it would be easier to catch men and women, he slowly walked to a village nearby. He went and sat on the edge of a muddy pond, waiting for someone to come by.

Many days passed by, but seeing the tiger, no one dared to come near the pond.

One day the tiger found a gold bangle. He knew that some people were very greedy. So he decided to use the gold bangle to trap greedy people and eat them.

He sat on the edge of the pond and whenever anyone came by, he would speak like a holy man, "Here is a gold bangle. Come and take it." But those who saw him would get scared and run away.

Then one day, a man came to the other side of the pond to get some water.

The tiger shouted, "Here is a gold bangle. Come and take it."

The man replied, "I want the bangle but I am afraid that you might kill me."

The tiger said, "I did kill in the past, but now I do not kill. I have sinned a lot. Now I want to be free of them. So every day, I take a bath in the pond and then give charity. Today, I want to give this gold bangle to you."

The man said, "I want to take the gold bangle but what if you kill me?"

The tiger said, "Just look at me. I am so weak and old and I cannot use my claws. Why do you fear me?"

The man believed the tiger and went into the pool to wade across to the tiger. But his feet got caught in the mud and he got stuck in the pond.

The man shouted, "Help me please. I am stuck. I can't move at all."

The tiger thought, "It is so good for me, my dear man, that you are greedy. Now I can really help you out or rather help myself."

The man shouted again, "Help me."

The tiger shouted, "Don't worry, man. I am here. I am coming to help you out. You listened to me and now I will listen to you, and come and help you."

And the tiger pounced upon the man. But the tiger did not help the man. It caught the man and jumped away from the pool to the other side.

Then the hungry tiger killed and ate the man, glad that the man had been greedy as well as very foolish.

The tiger then sat on the edge of the pond, with the gold bangle in his hand, waiting for another greedy man to come by.

THE CROWS' REVENGE

A crow and his wife lived on a banyan tree. They had been living there for a long time and were very happy.

Then one day, the female crow laid some eggs. Every morning, one of the crows would go out in search of food. The other would stay behind and look after the eggs.

One day they both went to look for food for themselves, leaving the eggs behind. A snake also lived there in a hole at the foot of the tree.

When the crows came back in the evening, they could not find their eggs in the nest. They looked here and there, then they understood what might have happened to the eggs.

The snake had slid up the tree and eaten all the eggs. This made the crows very sad, and they sat down and cried.

But the crows decided that they wouldn't give up. The female crow laid more eggs but the same thing happened to those eggs too.

This happened many times. Both the crows were very unhappy but they did not know what to do.

Then one day, the female crow said, "We must do something because the snake has eaten so many of our eggs. Let us leave this tree and go away to another tree."

The male crow said, "Why should we leave our tree? We have been living here for such a long time."

"Then what can we do? We cannot fight with the snake. It is so long and strong," said the female crow.

The male crow said, "Let us go to the clever jackal. He might tell us what we should do to get rid of the snake."

They told their story to the jackal who said, "You should not leave your tree because you have done no wrong. If somebody has to go, it should be the wicked snake. Let me think of a plan."

The crows waited quietly and then the jackal said, "I know what you should do."

"Go to the palace of the king. The princess, the daughter of the king, also lives there. When she goes for a bath in the morning, she removes her necklace and keeps it on the table," said the jackal.

"You have to pick up the necklace from there and drop it in the hole in which the snake lives," he added.

The next morning, the two crows went to the palace of the princess and picked up the necklace which she had kept on the table before her bath. The crows flew off with the necklace. The princess saw them and raised an alarm.

The royal guards ran after the crows who did as the jackal had said. They dropped the necklace in the snake's hole and sat right on the top of the tree.

The necklace fell on the snake and it came out from its hole to see what had happened. The guards saw the snake with the necklace.

They killed the snake with sharp spears. Then they picked up the necklace and took it to the princess.

The crows rejoiced, for now their eggs were safe, all thanks to the clever jackal.

A SHORT FRIENDSHIP

A cat, a rat and a mongoose lived near a banyan tree and an owl lived on the tree. The owl was afraid of the cat, and the mongoose was scared of both the cat and the owl. The rat was afraid of all of them.

One day, the cat got trapped in a net laid by a hunter under the tree.

The rat came and felt very happy to see the cat in the net. It started dancing and singing with happiness.

Just then the mongoose and the owl came and they saw the rat, just as the rat saw them.

The rat became scared as it knew that both the owl and the mongoose wanted to kill it. The rat had to make up its mind as to what it should do next.

The rat could not go to its house because the owl and the mongoose were in the way, ready to catch it.

The rat knew that the cat was its enemy but she was alone and in a net, while the owl and the mongoose were together, and both were its enemies. So the rat acted fast.

It took a risk and went inside the net and sat with the cat. The cat turned at once to kill the rat.

The rat said, "Please don't kill me. If you let me live then I will bite off the net with my sharp teeth and set you free."

Panchatantra

The cat wanted to be free from the net, so she did not kill the rat. The owl and the mongoose then went away when they saw that the rat was with the cat.

After the rat gnawed off the strings of the net, the cat was free from the net. The rat also quickly ran to its hole.

The cat came the next day to meet the rat, but the rat said, "I don't want to meet you because we are enemies."

The cat said, "Why won't you meet me? Yesterday, we had become friends."

The rat said, "We were friends for a short time. You saved me from my enemies and I saved you from the net."

The cat said, "So we are friends."

The rat said, "No, because enemies will always be enemies and there can be no trust between them. Our friendship was only for a short time. So let us stay just as we used to live earlier."

THE LION AND THE HARE

There lived a lion in a forest who was cruel to all the other animals. He would kill many of them at a time and eat them. He loved being called the king of all the animals.

One day, all the animals called a meeting to discuss how they could stop the lion from killing so many of them.

Panchatantra

Finally, they decided that they would tell the lion not to kill so many of them every day. They agreed to send one animal daily to the lion as his food.

The message was sent and the lion agreed. Every day an animal was sent as his dinner and the rest of the animals stopped being afraid till their turn came. One day, it was the turn of the clever hare.

The hare did not want to die. He wanted to save himself and the other animals. He had to do something. So he walked very slowly and reached the lion's den later than noon.

By that time, the lion was very angry. He shouted, "Why are you so late? Do you want me to kill all the animals?"

The hare said, "I am sorry, I am late but I could not help it."

The lion shouted, "Why?"

The hare said, "I was coming to you but then I saw another lion. I became very scared and I hid till the lion had left and then I came here. That lion calls himself the *king of the forest*."

The lion roared angrily, "Is there another lion in this forest? Does he call himself the king? Where is he? I will kill him."

The hare said, "Come with me, My Lord, and I will show you the lion."

The hare then led the lion to a well in the forest, but the lion could not see any other lion. He was all the more angry and shouted, "Where is that other lion?"

The hare pretended to look here and there as if looking for the other lion. He then peeped into the well and said, "The other lion is afraid of you, and so he is hiding from you. Look in the well and you will see him."

The lion peeped in the well and saw his own face in the water. But he thought that it was the other lion. He roared loudly and the well echoed the loud roar.

The lion thought that the other lion was roaring at him. He became so angry that he shouted, "I will kill you."

He jumped into the well and hit his head against the wall, and died.

Then the old hare went back to the other animals and told them that the lion was dead. They were all very happy and thanked the hare for freeing them from the cruel lion. Now they could live happily in peace, without any fear.

A jackal was very hungry. As he was looking for food, he saw a dead elephant. He was happy that he had found food, but there was a problem.

The jackal knew that the skin of the elephant would be too thick for his teeth. So, he wanted someone to make a cut in the skin of the dead elephant. But he did not want to share its flesh.

Just then a lion came and the clever jackal said, "I was guarding this elephant for you to taste. Please have a bite."

But the lion said, "No. I kill the animals myself and then eat them, and not the already dead ones." Saying this, the lion walked away. Then a tiger came there; the jackal was afraid that the tiger might eat the whole elephant.

The jackal said, "I am looking after this elephant because I don't want anyone to eat it."

The tiger walked to the elephant to eat it. Now the jackal was worried.

The jackal said, "Stop please. A hunter had killed this elephant with a poisoned arrow. Those who eat its flesh will also get poisoned."

That scared the tiger and he quickly went away. Then two vultures came and the jackal told the same thing to them. The vultures also flew away.

Then the jackal was happy that no one had taken away the dinner he had kept for himself. But he still needed the thick skin of the elephant to be cut before he could eat the flesh of the elephant.

Then a leopard came by.

The clever jackal said, "This elephant was killed by a lion who has gone to get his family to eat it."

The leopard said, "Oh! Then I should not have his dinner or he will be very angry with me."

The jackal then said, "Don't worry, I am your friend. I will help you."

The leopard asked, "But how?"

The jackal replied, "I will keep a watch. You can have a bite of the elephant. When I see the lion coming back, I will tell you and then, you can run away from here."

"How nice of you!" said the leopard and started biting the skin. When the jackal saw that the skin of the elephant had been cut by the leopard, he shouted, "The lion is coming."

The leopard left the dead elephant and ran away. This was what the jackal had wanted. The skin of the elephant had been cut by the leopard's sharp teeth. Now the jackal had his dinner and enjoyed the flesh for many days.

THE JACKAL GOES BLUE

A jackal was very hungry. When he could not get anything in the forest, he walked to a nearby village. As he entered the village, the dogs saw him and started barking. Then they began chasing the jackal.

46 *Panchatantra*

The jackal ran fast but from every side, the village dogs barked at him. The jackal was very frightened.

Just then, he saw the open door of a hut and ran straight into it. This was a washerman's house.

The jackal had been running very fast so he could not stop himself and fell into the pit of water, in which the washerman had put blue colour.

By then the dogs had stopped barking, so the jackal looked out of the door. The dogs had all gone away.

Now, he quickly but quietly ran to the forest. He was so thirsty that first he went to a pond to drink some water.

As he looked in the water, he got a shock. He had become blue. Then he saw that the other animals were also afraid of him because they had never seen a blue animal like him.

The jackal was very clever. He told one of the animals to get all the animals together.

When all the animals had gathered, he said, "God has sent me to look after you all. I am here to solve your problems, so that you all may live in peace. You all must respect me for I am your king."

All the animals believed him and started getting gifts for him. They obeyed whatever he said.

The jackal was having a wonderful time. He did not have to work or look for food. He just ordered everyone around and all the other animals did everything for him. Even the lions and tigers obeyed him and brought food for him.

The jackal enjoyed himself as the king of the forest. He had never been so happy. Now, he never went hungry.

But one day, he called for a big meeting. He was listening to the problems of the other animals when suddenly, he heard a pack of jackals howling outside. The blue jackal forgot that he was acting like a king. He could not stop himself and howled back.

All the animals were surprised. The jackal realised his mistake and became quiet. There was silence for a minute.

Then all the animals of the forest realised that the blue animal was just an ordinary jackal. They became angry and really beat him up for having fooled them for so many days.

A tortoise lived near a river. It walked slowly but talked endlessly. It had two geese for friends. They enjoyed each other's company and had a nice time.

One particular summer, it didn't rain at all. The sun was so hot that all the rivers and lakes dried up.

The river near which the three friends lived also became dry. They had to search here and there for water to drink. It was not an easy task to do in the scorching heat of the sun.

So the three friends sat thinking as to what should be done. They looked around the place everywhere but could not find water anywhere nearby. So they planned to move to another lake.

They realised walking would not help since all the nearby ponds and lakes had dried up. So, they had to fly.

The problem was that the geese could fly but the tortoise could not fly.

The tortoise said, "I have a plan. Get a stick and you both hold it at the two ends with your beaks, and I will hold the stick in the centre with my mouth."

One goose said, "This plan is good but dangerous because you talk a lot and can't keep quiet for long."

The other goose said, "If you open your mouth to talk while we are flying, then you will fall off the stick on the ground."

The tortoise said, "Yes, you both are right. If I fall, I will surely die. But don't worry. I will keep quiet."

So they got hold of a stick. One goose held it in its beak at one end, and the other one held the stick at the other end. The tortoise caught the stick with his mouth in the centre and they flew up. They flew over forests and hills, valleys and rivers, and when they passed over a city, many people looked at them curiously.

It was indeed a strange sight to see the two geese and a tortoise holding a stick and flying.

The people of the town had never seen such a thing so they started clapping and shouting.

The geese were worried that now the tortoise would start talking. They wanted to tell him not to talk. But they could not leave the stick, so they kept quiet.

The tortoise heard the people shouting. He tried to look down but could not see what was happening.

Finally, the tortoise could not stop himself. He wanted to ask, "What is this noise?"

But when he opened his mouth to say this, he left the stick. The tortoise fell from the sky onto the ground and died. The poor geese could not do anything to save the foolish tortoise from falling on the ground below. They realised that they had lost their friend forever.

Once a stork lived near a pond. The stork was a big bird with a long neck and a long beak. There were many fish in the pond and the stork would eat many of them every day. He never went hungry.

However, over the years, the stork became old and slow.

It was not easy for him to catch fish because they were quick and would swim away. The stork now had to stay hungry quite often. So he thought of a plan that would get him food every day.

The next day, he stood on one foot. He did not try to catch fish but pretended to look very sad.

The fish were surprised that the stork was not trying to catch them.

One young fish was very bold. She asked the stork, "What is the matter? Why are you so sad? Why aren't you catching us today? Are you not hungry?"

The stork replied, "I am hungry but am feeling very sad. I pity you all."

"But why?" asked the curious fish.

"A fisherman is coming here to catch you all in his big net," said the stork.

"This is bad news," said the fish

Then the stork said, "Don't worry. I can help you. Though I am old, I will take you one by one to the other pond, where you will be safe and happy."

The fish thought that it was a good idea because it would save them from the cruel fisherman and his net. So, they all agreed to the stork's plan.

The stork would pick up the fish and fly away. Then he would eat the fish and come back for another. He also left some of the fish on the ground to dry.

Meanwhile, a clever crab had been observing the stork carrying the fish. He went to the stork and said, "Why don't you take me also to the other pond?"

The stork was fed up of eating fish every day, so he readily agreed to take the crab, for he loved crab meat.

The crab was too big to stay in the stork's mouth, so the crab said, "Let me sit on your neck." The stork agreed.

As the stork flew, the crab looked down and saw some dead fish lying on the ground. He also saw fish bones.

The crab realised that the stork was not good and helpful, but had killed the poor fish. So he thought of a plan to punish the evil stork.

He told the stork, "It is so nice of you to save me but I feel I should save my family also. Let us go back and I will show you where they are."

The stork was greedy and thought that he would get some more crabs to eat. So he turned around to go back to the pond which they had left behind.

The stork asked, "Tell me, where is your family, crab?"

"Near the pond where we met," said the clever crab.

"So we should go to the pond and bring your family here," said the stork.

"It is so nice of you that you are helping me to save my family," said the crab.

"It is my duty," said the greedy stork, and he turned back to fly to the pond.

They were very near to the pond now.

The crab said, "I also have a duty to do. You told the fish that you would help them. But you have been killing all the fish. I have to end the life of such a bad stork, as you have turned out to be."

Just as they reached the pond, the crab bit the stork's neck hard. The head of the stork fell off.

The dead stork and the crab fell down onto the ground. The crab got a bit hurt, but he was happy that he had done a good deed. He went and told the fish how the stork had killed the other fish.

They were sad for the dead fish but glad that such a bad stork was dead at last, and would never trouble them again. They all thanked the crab for saving their lives. They also pledged never to trust anyone blindly.

There lived a poor man in a village. He had some land in the village but though he toiled day and night, nothing would grow on the land.

One day, while he was working on his land, he felt very tired. So he fell asleep under a tree.

When he woke up, the poor man was quite surprised to see a snake peeping out of a hole in the ground under the tree. The snake hissed at him.

The farmer thought, "Oh! Now I know what the matter is. The king cobra lives here and I have never fed him milk. So he is angry with me and does not let anything grow on my land."

The farmer then ran to his hut and brought a bowl of milk for the king cobra. He sat down nearby and prayed for money and happiness.

The cobra drank the milk and said to the farmer, "I am very happy with you. Get me a bowl of milk every day."

The farmer bent down to pick up the empty bowl and was astonished to see a gold coin in it. The farmer was overjoyed and he thanked the snake.

From that day onwards, the farmer gave a bowl of milk to the cobra and got a gold coin in return daily. Slowly, his fields were full of crops and he became rich.

Besides continuing to grow crops, the farmer gradually started a business in the nearby town. He was happy and had a lot of money.

Once the farmer had to go to a far off city to buy some seeds for his farm. He told his son to give the cobra a bowl of milk every day.

The young son of the farmer gave a bowl of milk the next day, and saw the gold coin in the bowl. He felt very happy.

He looked at the snake and wondered. "If the snake takes out the gold coins from its stomach, then it must be having lots of them in his stomach," thought the greedy boy.

He went on keeping the bowl of milk every day and getting the gold coins.

One day, he thought, "It is foolish to collect only one gold coin every day. Why don't I take all the gold coins in one day?"

So the next day, the farmer's son gave a bowl of milk to the cobra. The cobra finished the milk, and as was the daily routine, left a gold coin in the bowl.

As the cobra turned to go back in the hole, the farmer's son cut off the snake's neck with an axe. He then ripped open the stomach of the snake, but was shocked to find no gold coin there.

He then realised his mistake. His greed had blinded him, and he knew that now he would not get any gold coins ever.

A BROKEN FRIENDSHIP

One day, a cow wandered off and lost its way back to the village where it lived, and instead reached a forest. There the cow met a lioness. They became friends and were very happy together. After some time, the cow gave birth to a bull calf and the lioness gave birth to a cub. Both the babies grew up playing together and became true friends.

A woodcutter saw the bull and the lion playing together, and went to tell the king about this unusual thing.

The king said to the woodcutter, "When you see a third animal with these two friends, then come and tell me."

The woodcutter returned after a few days and told the king that now a jackal also stayed with the bull and the lion.

The wise king said, "Now the jackal will not let them be friends. He will make them fight. So, let us go to the forest."

The king was right. The jackal went first to the lion and said, "The bull is not your friend. He speaks ill about you behind your back."

And then the jackal went to the bull and told the same thing to the bull. Both the bull and the lion were foolish and believed what the jackal said.

Instead of talking to each other and finding out the truth, they blindly believed the cunning jackal.

The deep friendship of the bull and the lion ended because of the jackal. They started disliking each other.

One day, a big fight ensued between the lion and the bull, and both fought fiercely. They both were badly hurt and soon died.

This is what the jackal had wanted.

Actually, he wanted to eat the flesh of the lion and the bull because he had never eaten such flesh before.

Panchatantra

For his own selfish motive, he had created rift between the two good friends.

When the king came to the forest, he saw the jackal eating the flesh of the lion and the bull.

The king felt sorry that the bull and the lion had not trusted each other. They had believed whatever the jackal had told them about each other.

The king was very angry with the jackal for turning the two good friends into bitter enemies.

So he picked up his bow and arrow, and aimed at the jackal. The jackal did not see the king because he was busy eating the flesh of the bull and the lion.

The arrow hit the jackal and he died at once. The king went back to his palace still feeling sad about the broken friendship between the lion and the bull.

A washerman needed a donkey to carry the load of clothes from his hut to the river and back.

The washerman found a donkey roaming in the nearby forest. He took it home, but was too poor to feed it. And it seemed as if the donkey was always hungry.

The donkey was lazy and would not go anywhere far to find something to eat.

Once the washerman had to go to the city to buy things. When he was returning home, he had to cross the forest.

As he was passing through the forest, he saw the skin of a leopard. The washerman brought the leopard's skin home. Then he thought of a plan.

He wanted to use the leopard's skin to feed his donkey. When it was night, he put the leopard's skin on the donkey and took him to the fields.

The watchmen saw the donkey with the leopards' skin. They thought that a leopard had actually come into their field. They ran away from the field, afraid that the leopard would eat them.

Alone in the big field, the donkey ate as much as he could. He felt nice and happy after eating to his heart's content.

This went on for many months and the donkey became fat. But one night, when the washerman left him in the field to eat his fill, the donkey heard another donkey braying from the far off village.

The stupid donkey forgot that he had the skin of a leopard on him. He just lifted his head and started braying, "Dheychoon, dheychoon."

The watchmen now realised that the leopard was in fact, a donkey. They were furious at having been fooled by a donkey.

They came to the field with big sticks and beat the donkey till he turned black and blue. Then the donkey ran for his life and was never seen again.

A jackal was always hungry, but was too lazy to attack and kill animals himself.

He would lay around waiting to find a dead animal to satisfy his hunger. As he had not found any dead animal for a long time, he was very hungry.

So one day, in order to find some food for himself, he walked out of the forest.

After wandering for a while, he came across a battlefield. There he found a huge drum which might have been used by soldiers to announce the start of a battle.

The jackal looked at the drum. A small branch fell on it and there was a loud 'dhummm' sound.

The jackal was frightened by the sound and screaming, 'Oooooooh' with fright, he ran away from the drum.

But then he saw that the drum was not moving but remained where it was.

Slowly, the jackal went closer and hit the drum.

The sound of 'dhummmm' came again. Now the jackal thought that there was another animal inside the big drum. As he was thinking, a leopard happened to come by, looking around for food.

The jackal called the leopard and said, "I think there is an animal inside the drum. If you can open the drum, you may catch the animal and eat it." The leopard was also hungry, so he began clawing at the drum.

Panchatantra

'Dhhhummmm,' the drum made a loud noise, and the frightened leopard shouted, 'Aaaoooow' and ran away from the drum.

The jackal ran up to him and said, "Don't be afraid. There is an animal inside the drum who is making this noise. You can have the animal for your meal."

The leopard then tore open the drum. But there was no animal inside.

The leopard shouted at the jackal, "Where is the animal? You have told me lies and wasted my time. Now you will have to pay for it."

The angry leopard pounced on the jackal and killed him with one strong blow. He ate up the dead jackal and walked away.

THE BIRD THAT DROPPED GRAINS OF GOLD

Once a lovely little bird lived on a tree. Every time the bird sang in its melodious voice, grains of gold would fall from its mouth.

One day, a man who caught birds, saw this unique bird. He was surprised that when it sang, grains of gold fell from its mouth.

The man decided to catch the bird and keep it with him.

He put a net under the tree and threw some rice grains on the ground. The bird saw the grains of rice and flew down to eat them. The bird got caught in the net and the man took it home.

In his house, the bird would sing, and grains of gold would fall. Soon the man had collected a lot of gold.

He became a rich man. But then he thought, "Am I doing the right thing by keeping the bird here? What if the king comes to know about it?"

He became worried as he thought, "I might get punished, or even killed for not telling the king about the bird. However, if I present the bird to the king myself, he might become happy and give me a reward."

The man took the bird in its cage and went to the king. When the man told the king about the little bird dropping grains of gold, the king was very happy.

The king rewarded the man handsomely. He then got a gold cage made for the bird.

Every morning, the bird would sing and grains of gold would drop from its mouth. Thus the king became richer and richer day by day.

But one day, the prime minister of the kingdom said, "My Lord! Don't keep this bird. Let it go."

The king asked, "Why?"

The prime minister said, "How can a bird drop gold from its mouth? There must be something bad about it too. It might cause your death or your family's death. It may be unlucky. Just don't keep it in your palace. Let the bird go."

The king agreed with the prime minister. He ordered the bird to be set free. The bird flew and sat on the roof of the palace of the king.

The bird shouted from the top, "There are four fools in this kingdom. First I was a fool that I went to eat rice grains and got caught in the net. The second fool was the man who caught me. He did not keep me with him, but gave me to the king. The third is the prime minister who advised the king to set me free. And the fourth, and the biggest fool of all, is the king who acted on the prime minister's advice without thinking. So I won't stay here anymore. I am going."

The bird then flew away high into the sky, to the mountains, never to return again.

A GOAT OR A GHOST

A man was asked by his old father to purchase a goat from the market in the village nearby.

The man went to the village and bought a fat goat. He lifted the goat on his shoulders and started walking back home, very happy with the purchase. Three thieves began to follow him.

These three thieves had been roaming in the market to steal something. They saw this man with the goat, and they came after him, planning to take the goat.

One of the thieves came up to this man and said, "Why are you carrying a dog on your shoulders?"

The man said, "Are you blind? It is not a dog. It is a goat."

The first thief said, "Sorry, but I just told you what I saw."

After some time, the second thief walked up to the man and said, "Why are you carrying a dead calf on your shoulders?"

The man said, "It is a living goat, not a dead calf."

The second thief said, "You don't know what animal you are carrying. I only told you what I saw."

A little later, the third thief came laughing and said to the man, "Why have you got a donkey on your shoulders? Are you out of your mind? People will laugh at you."

Now the man was really really upset. He wondered, "What am I carrying? One man says it is a dog, the other says it is a dead calf and the third says it is a donkey. Is it a goat or a ghost who keeps changing its form. I must get rid of it now."

The man threw the goat down and ran for his life, afraid that the ghost might come after him. After some time, three thieves took the goat away. They had got what they wanted.

An elephant was not liked at all by the other animals. He was very huge and did not care for anyone. He was cruel and would hurt others often.

He would be so angry at times, that he would pull down trees because of which many nests, with eggs in them, would fall down and break.

All the animals stayed away from him because he could harm and kill the animals at his will. He walked around, with his big feet crushing the burrows of the animals.

The foxes, in particular, were very upset with him because many of their houses had been blown away by the wicked elephant.

So, they called a meeting to find a solution to the problem.

They all agreed that the elephant was too huge for them to kill. What was needed, was a clever plan to keep the elephant out of the way.

The cleverest fox assured everyone that he would surely do something. He went after the elephant and observed what he did the whole day long.

Then next day, the fox went and stood in front of the elephant.

He bowed to him and said, "My Lord. It is very important that I talk to you."

The elephant shouted rudely, "Who are you?"

The fox said, "All the animals have sent me to ask you something."

The elephant retorted, "Hurry up, tell me what you want. Don't waste my time."

The fox said, "All the animals want to crown you our king, My Lord."

The elephant was very happy for he had always wanted to be the king.

The fox said, "Please come for the ceremony where we will crown you, and then you will be our king. This will be done in the middle of the forest, so that all the animals can witness this."

The elephant said, "Wait, let me see if I am looking nice," and he went to the pond to see his image in the water.

"Come on, let us go," he said walking like a proud king.

The fox walked ahead and the elephant followed him. The fox took him to a place where there was a lot of wet mud. The fox cleverly stepped aside to avoid the mud but the elephant was walking with his head held high up in the air, like a king.

He did not see the wet mud and his feet sank right into it. As he was too heavy and big, he got stuck in the wet mud.

The elephant called, "Dear fox, help me out. I have got stuck here."

The fox just laughed, shaking his head.

Then the elephant shouted, "As your king, I order you to save me."

The fox laughed louder, "You can never be our king. I told you lies to get you stuck here in the wet mud. You are bad. You have been cruel to everyone. You have pulled down trees and plants."

"Please take me out of here, foxy, please," pleaded the elephant.

The fox said, "You never cared for anyone, now why should I care for you?"

"Please, please foxy, save me," the scared elephant pleaded some more.

The fox said, "We asked you to be kind and begged you not to be cruel. See how it feels. Now you are begging for your life but I will not save you because you have hurt and killed many of us. Stay here in the wet mud."

Then the fox went away. All the animals who came that way, saw the stuck elephant, but no one helped him.

The elephant thought, "Oh! why was I so cruel? Had I been kind, they would have helped me." The wicked elephant drowned to death in the muddy water.

A deer and a crow lived near each other in a forest. They saw each other daily but were not friendly with each other.

The deer thought that the crow was not nice because it was black and ugly. The crow thought that the deer was too beautiful to look at, so he must be proud and rude.

Both the crow and the deer remained aloof because they thought that they would not get along well with each other. So, they never tried to speak with one another.

One day, they had a conversation and started liking each other a lot. The deer now loved to be with the crow, who would sit on his back and cry 'caw caw', all day.

They would talk for a long time, and now both of them became good friends.

One day, a jackal came by and looking at the deer, said, "You are really very beautiful. Your skin is lovely and your flesh must be healthy and sweet too."

The deer thanked the jackal. They started meeting again and again. The jackal would narrate many humorous incidents, and the deer liked the way the jackal made him laugh. The deer now began to spend more time with the jackal than with the crow.

One day, the jackal said, "You run very fast and are very strong. You should eat good food to keep good health."

The deer replied, "I am happy with what I eat."

The jackal insisted, "You should eat sweet corn. That would be very good for you. There is a field full of sweet corn. I will take you there."

The deer agreed and went with the jackal to the field, where the deer got caught in a net laid by the farmers.

The deer told the jackal, "I am caught in a net. Please save me. You can bite the net off with your sharp teeth."

The jackal said, "But I am fasting today, and cannot touch anything with my teeth. I will come tomorrow when my fast is over, then I will free you."

The deer said, "So you are not my friend. You planned to trap me."

The jackal said, "Yes, I always wanted to taste your juicy flesh. By tomorrow, you will be dead." And the jackal went away.

The deer felt bad that he had trusted the jackal. Then he heard a sound, 'caw, caw.' He looked up to see his old friend, the crow, sitting on a branch of a tree.

The deer thought, "Will the crow be my true friend and save me, or will he also betray my trust like the jackal?"

The crow asked, "How did you get caught in this net?"

The deer replied, "The jackal tricked me. He is not my true friend. The farmer will soon be here. I must escape at once."

The crow said, "I will tell you what to do. You lie down as if you are dead. When I see the farmer remove the net, I will cry, 'caw caw', and you can run away."

So the deer lay down without any movement. He closed his eyes when he heard the footsteps of the farmer coming.

Suddenly, the crow cried aloud, 'caw caw.' Then the deer quickly jumped up and ran away.

The farmer threw his big stick at the deer but the stick did not hit the deer.

On the other hand, it hit the jackal who had come to check on the deer. In fact, the stick hit the head of the jackal and he fell down, never to get up again.

The deer ran home quickly, so that the farmer could not catch him. The crow flew to its tree, all the while flying over the running deer. Then they reached the forest where they lived.

They sat down to rest and the deer gratefully said to the crow, "Thank you so much for helping me."

The crow said, "Don't thank me. If you were in my place, I am sure you would have done the same thing. The fact is that we both are friends and we will always be there to help and look after each other."

THE MONKEY'S HEART

Once a crocodile became friendly with a monkey. The crocodile would lie under the sun on the bank of the river and the monkey would sit on his mango tree.

They would spend hours talking with each other. The monkey kept eating mangoes and also gave some to the crocodile to eat.

The monkey came to know that the crocodile had a wife on the other side of the river. So he gave some mangoes to the crocodile for his wife too.

The crocodile's wife ate the mangoes and asked her husband, "Where did you get these delicious mangoes from?"

The crocodile said, "I have a friend, the monkey. He lives on a mango tree and keeps eating mangoes, and gives them to me too. He is very nice and has sent some mangoes for you."

The wife said, "If the monkey eats such sweet mangoes, then his heart must be sweet too. I want to eat his heart. Please bring it for me."

The crocodile was shocked and said, "The monkey is my friend, how can I kill him? To eat his heart, he will have to be killed."

"You care for the monkey more than me. You have to get his heart or I will go away," replied his greedy wife.

After some time, the poor crocodile agreed and swam to the monkey.

"My wife loved the mangoes but she was saying that I should have invited you home for dinner," the crocodile said.

"That is very kind of her but your home is on the other side of the river and I can't swim. How will I reach there?" asked the monkey.

"You can sit on my back and I will swim," said the crocodile.

The monkey took some more mangoes for the crocodile's wife and sat on the back of the crocodile. They were in the middle of the river when the monkey said, "Please slow down. I am not used to water. I might fall and drown."

"Your end is near anyway. You have to die," said the crocodile.

"What do you mean?" asked the surprised monkey.

"My wife wants to eat your heart," said the crocodile, thinking that there was no harm in telling the truth to the monkey because he could not swim.

The monkey said, "But why didn't you tell me before? Then I would have brought my heart with me. I have kept it in a hole in the mango tree. Now, how will your wife eat my heart?"

"We must go back then so that you can get your heart," said the crocodile.

So the crocodile quickly swam back to the mango tree, where the wise monkey lived. The monkey then jumped onto the bank and climbed his tree.

He knew that crocodiles could not climb trees, so he was safe. The crocodile said, "Hurry up monkey."

The monkey said, "You are such a fool. How can I keep my heart away from my body? I had it all the time with me. Now I am never coming down near you."

The crocodile could do nothing. He slowly swam away, knowing that he had lost a very good friend, forever.

Once a partridge left his hole in the ground to go and look for some rice grains to store them to eat during the harsh winter months.

The partridge was gone for many days. Meanwhile, a hare happened to come by. When he saw the unoccupied hole of the partridge, he decided to make it his home and comfortably settled in.

When the partridge returned, he found the hare was living in that hole. Now both the partridge and the hare began fighting over the hole.

The partridge said that he had lived there for long, so it was his hole. The hare also said that he, who was living at that time, owned the hole. The partridge asked the hare to get out of his home but the hare did not budge from there.

Many animals witnessed their quarrel but no one could find out whose home it was. So both of them agreed to go to a wise person to arrive at a solution.

After a while, they reached the banks of a river and saw a big cat standing there.

The partridge thought that the cat would be very good and wise. But the hare said, "I don't like this big cat. I am afraid that she might eat me up."

The cat heard this and told the hare not to fear her.

Panchatantra

The cat said, "I am not like other cats. I don't even eat meat. I love to pray and help others."

The partridge began telling the cat about the quarrel between them. She told the cat that he had gone away from the house only for a few days.

The hare then tried to justify himself. By now both the hare and the partridge had started trusting the big cat.

After the cat had heard both of them, she said, "I am old, so I couldn't hear everything very clearly. Come closer and tell me your stories again."

The two went closer and the cat pounced on them and caught both the partridge and the hare with her sharp claws.

Because of their quarrel for the hole, the partridge and the hare became an easy prey for the big cat. They wrongly placed their trust on the cat. They had to pay with their lives for the blind faith they invested in the cat.

THE FROG AND THE SNAKE

A frog lived in a well with his friends and relatives. He was the king of all the frogs but some of them revolted against him.

Somehow the frog cleverly settled everything. But he was very angry with his relatives, so one day, he came out of his well alone and went to the black snake who lived in a hole nearby.

Panchatantra

The snake was surprised to see the frog standing in front of him, for he knew that frogs were afraid of him.

The frog said, "I want to be your friend."

The snake said, "But we have always been enemies, then how can we be friends?"

The frog said, "First, please hear my plan. My relatives have created a lot of problems for me, so I want to punish them. You can come into my well and eat them."

The snake agreed and one by one the snake ate up all the friends and relatives of the king frog.

Then he said to the frog, "I have eaten all your relatives, except your family. Now, I will have to eat you and your wife and children."

The frog realised that he had made a mistake; to punish his own people, he had brought an enemy into his kingdom. Now he had to do something quickly to save his family.

So the frog said, "Don't worry. I will get more frogs for you tomorrow. My family will go and collect all of them for you."

The snake became happy and the family of the frog jumped out of the well, never to come back to that well again.

There were three fish sisters who lived in a pond with their family, relatives and friends.

One day, the sisters overheard some fishermen talking, "There are many fish here in this pond. Let us come here and catch them all."

After the fishermen had gone, the fish discussed about the danger of being caught by the fishermen.

The eldest sister thought for a while and said that they should leave that pond and go somewhere else to save themselves from the fishermen.

The middle sister also thought that it was better to vacate the pond than to get caught by the fishermen and die.

But the youngest sister was lazy and carefree. She said, "Why should we leave our house? Let the fishermen come. We will not be caught in their.net. Maybe the fishermen won't come at all!"

But the two elder sisters said to the youngest one, "You do what you want to, but we both are going through that stream there, to the other pond."

The two elder sisters got their family together and asked others too to come with them.

However, the youngest sister just wanted to stay in their own pond. Many fish advised her to change her mind.

However, she did not listen to anyone. Nonetheless, there were still many fish, who stayed behind with the youngest sister in this pond which had always been their home.

The next morning, the fishermen came. They threw their nets and caught many fish. The youngest sister was also caught by the fishermen.

Her two elder sisters felt very sad about it. They wished that the youngest one too had been wise and kept herself safe from the fishermen.

The sisters thought how wonderful it would have been if their youngest sister had listened to them and had come with them.

But the youngest one chose not to be careful, and so she was lost to them forever. If only she had been less stubborn and had obeyed them, she would still have been alive.

FOUR FRIENDS AND THE LION

There were four men who had been friends since their childhood. When they grew up, they wanted to go out of their village to earn more money.

Three of them had studied a lot, but the fourth one, had not studied so much. However, he had a lot of common sense.

The four friends decided to go to a big city to make a lot of money.

Panchatantra

They had to pass through a forest on their way to the city. As they were walking through the forest, they saw the bones of a lion lying under a tree.

The three, who had studied a lot, stopped and said that they wanted to test their skills and knowledge. They would try to get the lion back to life. The three sat down and started trying to bring the lion to life.

The first one arranged the bones in the shape of a lion's body. Then he chanted something and the bones joined together to form the skeleton of the lion.

The second then put some flesh, skin and blood in the lion. Now it looked like a lion, but had no life.

The third said, "I will try and put life in this lion."

The fourth friend said, "Wait. Don't do it. I may not have read many books, but I know that if you put life in the lion, it will act like any other lion and eat us."

The other three would not listen. Then the fourth friend ran to a nearby tree.

He climbed on to a high branch of the tree.

The three laughed that the fourth one was so afraid. Then the third one sat down and tried to put life in the lion.

As soon as he uttered his chant, the lion became alive again and roared at the three friends. Now the three men felt that they were in danger.

They realised that the fourth one had been the cleverest of them because he had thought of what would happen and had climbed up the tree.

The three men now tried to run away, but the lion roared loudly and attacked them.

Only the fourth man, who had gone up the tree, was saved.

Then the fourth one thought, "Studying many books is good, but with that, it is also important that we think cleverly with our mind."

He sadly looked at his three dead friends and thought, "I had studied less than these three, but I am safe. Why? What does this prove?"

He thought about it and then said to himself, "Yes, I know. Just studying books is not enough. We should be clever too and think wisely before we do anything in our life. And that is what I have done. This is called common sense because of which I am safe."

UGLY AND BEAUTIFUL

A stag looked at his reflection in the water. Many animals had told him that he was very handsome. He found the antlers on his head to be very beautiful and his thin legs to be ugly.

As he was admiring himself, he heard a lion roar, 'Aaaah!' right behind him.

He ran from there. The lion chased the stag but he ran faster.

Panchatantra

The stag ran so fast that the lion was left far behind. After a while, the stag stopped.

He thought, "I was thinking that my legs are thin and don't look nice. But these legs have helped me to run away from the lion and have thus, saved my life."

Suddenly, he heard the lion's roar again. He knew that he was again in danger. He got up to run but his antlers got caught in the low branches of a tree.

He tried to free himself, but to no avail. His antlers were completely stuck in the branches.

The stag thought, "How strange! I was thinking that my antlers are beautiful. But now these antlers have got me into trouble by getting caught in the branches of this tree. What I thought to be ugly, that is, my legs, had helped me. Hence, we should never judge things by their looks but their qualities."

The lion roared again and in one big leap, pounced on the helpless deer.

A little mouse lived in a forest. He was happy that he had a home and enough to eat. He would also go to listen to a holy man's sermons.

This famous holy man lived in the forest and preached to all the animals of the forest.

One day, the mouse was going to the holy man. Suddenly, he heard a sound, 'meeaow' and a big cat jumped on him.

The mouse just ran away as fast as he could. The cat chased him but he ran faster to the holy man and told him the whole story. The cat also reached there and was about to pounce on the mouse, when the holy man changed him into a bigger cat. Seeing the mouse become a bigger cat, the other cat ran away, scared.

Now the mouse as a cat, had a lot of fun. He troubled all those animals who had troubled him when he was a mouse. He even shouted 'meeeeaooow' at the other mice and fought with the other cats who had hurt him before.

But one day, a fox shouted, 'Oooaaooo' and jumped on him. The mouse–cat then realised that bigger animals could trouble a cat too! He managed to save himself and ran to the holy man again.

Chasing the cat, the fox too reached the holy man.

This time the holy man changed the mouse into a bigger fox. So the other fox ran away, scared of the bigger fox.

The mouse-fox had a wonderful time and was really happy being a fox.

But then one day, a tiger jumped on him and he got scared. He ran to the holy man again and this time the holy man changed him into a bigger tiger.

Now this mouse-tiger thought that he was the king of the forest. He felt he was very strong and started troubling the other animals.

He lived like a king and made the others obey him. He did all he wanted to and felt very happy when he saw that everyone was scared of him. He would roar, 'AAAaaaaaaaw' at everyone.

But one thing always troubled him. He was afraid that the holy man could change him into a mouse anytime. So he thought that he would go and talk to the holy man himself and settle this.

He told the holy man, "I want to eat you because I am hungry. I also want your holy powers with which you can change animals from a mouse into a cat, into a fox or into a tiger."

Now the holy man became very angry. He shouted, "I was helping you because I thought that others were troubling you. But you have become so proud that you even want to eat me, the person who has always helped you."

The holy man then changed the tiger back into a mouse again.

The mouse thought, "What fun it had been as a big cat. It was better as a fox and it was the best, being a tiger."

Now that he had become a mouse again, he felt that he had lost everything. He felt very sorry and wondered why he had acted in such a foolish manner.

He should have been a good cat, then a good fox and a better tiger.

He knew that he had done a big mistake in wanting to kill the holy man who had helped him so much.

The mouse apologised to the holy man. He didn't like it when his voice came out as a soft, 'chu chu chu'. So he asked the holy man to make him a tiger again, so that he could roar, 'Aaaaaaaaa' again.

But the holy man refused saying, "I don't trust you at all any more."

When the mouse kept on begging, the holy man picked up a stick. He ran after the mouse and drove him away.

The mouse realised that day that he had wasted a golden chance to be big and powerful. So, he went about the forest trying to save himself from the bigger animals, just as before.

TRUE FRIENDS

There were four friends who lived in a forest: a black crow, a small mouse, a tortoise and a deer. They were all very happy living together near a pond, and they really got along well with each other.

One day, the crow, the mouse and the tortoise waited for the deer, but he did not turn up.

They were worried that something bad had happened to the deer.

The crow quickly flew around the forest and soon saw the deer, who was caught in a trap laid by a hunter.

The crow flew down to the deer and said, "Oh! My poor friend. Shall I call the other friends?"

"Yes, call them quickly before the hunter comes," said the scared deer.

The crow flew back quickly and told the mouse and the tortoise.

The tortoise suggested, "The mouse should go and gnaw the net."

"But I am so small. How will I find my way to the deer?" asked the mouse.

The crow replied, "Sit on my back."

The mouse sat on the crow's back and the crow flew as fast as he could to the deer. The crow then flew back to the tortoise. He too sat on the crow's back and they soon reached the deer.

The mouse had, meanwhile started gnawing the net.

Soon, the deer was free and he thanked his friends.

The four of them held each other and were glad to be back together. They were really happy that they were able to save the deer from the hunter.

But suddenly, they heard some footsteps, 'Thup thup thump thump.'

The deer shouted, "The hunter is coming. Quick. Hide."

The mouse went into a hole. The crow flew to the top of a tree and the deer ran away into the forest. But the poor tortoise was slow. He could not move fast though he tried very hard.

The hunter reached the spot and found his net cut. He was further infuriated when he could not see the deer anywhere.

Then he saw this tortoise who had quickly pulled his head, hands and feet inside his shell.

The hunter picked up the tortoise and kept it in his bag. The crow saw all this from the tree. He quickly flew, and told the mouse and the deer of what had happened.

The mouse advised, "We should do something quickly before the hunter reaches home."

The deer ran fast and stood in clear view of the hunter to distract him.

The hunter, on seeing the deer, threw down the bag with the tortoise and ran after the deer to catch him.

Meanwhile, the mouse and the crow quickly helped the tortoise out of the bag.

The deer ran so fast that the hunter could not catch him. When the hunter came back to the tortoise, he found him to be gone too. Angry and sad, the hunter went home empty handed. He had not only been unable to catch any animal, but had lost his net too.

JOY RIDE OR DEATH?

A snake had become old and weak, and it was not easy for him to catch animals for his food.

So he thought of a plan. He went and lay down near the pond where a lot of frogs lived. There he began to behave as if he was very ill, "Hiiisss Hiisss Hissss."

The king frog came out to see the snake. He was afraid but he asked the snake, "What is the matter?"

The snake replied, "The son of a holy man was hitting me with a stick and I retaliated by biting him."

The king frog felt even more scared. Had this snake come to bite and eat them? Should they go away at once?

The snake continued, "The holy man then cursed me. He said that I have to serve frogs, and I would have to eat whatever the frogs give me and nothing else. So I have come to serve you all. Tell me what can I do for you?"

Now the king frog was not afraid. He was happy. He loved to sail so he told the snake to go into the pond. The king frog then sat on the back of the snake and the snake swam around.

Throughout the day, the frogs took joy rides on the snake's back. At the end of the day, the snake pretended to be tired.

The king frog saw that the snake had become slower and slower.

He then asked the snake, "What is the matter?"

The snake replied, "I have not eaten anything so I am feeling weak and tired. I can't move."

The king frog said, "But I want another joy ride. I really love it."

"But I am weak and hungry. And there is nothing to eat here. There are only frogs everywhere," replied the snake.

"All right. Eat a few frogs, but give me a joy ride," said the selfish king frog.

The snake was very happy as he ate one frog and then another. In the end, only the king frog was left and there was nobody to save him.

The snake said, "I am still very hungry. I have to eat you, king frog."

The king frog now realised that he should not have trusted a snake, who is a frog's enemy. Alas! it was too late! The snake gobbled up the king frog too.

THE FISHY TRAP

A family of cranes lived on a tree. At the foot of the tree, there also lived a cruel black snake who would eat all the young ones of birds and animals who played there.

One day, the crab saw a crane crying bitterly.

The crab asked, "Why are you crying, Aunt Crane?"

The crane replied, "This snake is troubling all the children of this area. What can we do?"

The crab said, "This is the rule of the forest, Aunt. Don't cry. We all eat each other. Here you have to be strong so that you can stay alive."

"I am worried about the children and not myself," said the crane.

The crab nodded, "All right. Let me think."

The next day, the crab came and called all the cranes living on the tree to tell them about a plan.

The crab said, "We small animals cannot do anything to harm the snake. You are big cranes, but the snake is very bad and might hurt you."

A crane asked, "Is there no way to get the snake away from here?"

"There is a way. That is why I have come."

"We should request the old mongoose to kill the snake because they are enemies," said the clever crab.

"But the mongoose stays in his hole all the time. How will we get him out of it?" asked the crane.

The crab replied, "The mongoose loves fish. You all are very good at catching fish. Catch some fish and keep it for the mongoose."

"And then?" asked the curious crane.

The clever crab replied, "Place the fish in a line, at some distance from each other. Leave one fish in front of the hole of the mongoose. Then the second one, the third and so on, till the hole of the snake."

So the cranes caught six fish and kept them in a line from the hole of the mongoose to the hole of the snake. And then, they waited for the mongoose.

Guess what the mongoose did? He came out of his hole and saw the fish. He started eating the fish one by one.

He ate till he reached the last one near the hole of the snake.

The cranes were now waiting to see if the mongoose would go near the snake. The mongoose ate the last fish and turned back. Suddenly, he sniffed something.

The mongoose started looking around searching for the snake whom he had smelt.

The mongoose rushed into the snake's hole. The cranes could hear the snake and the mongoose fighting.

Soon, the mongoose came out of the hole, with the dead snake in his mouth.

The cranes thanked the wise crab for his wonderful plan that helped them to get rid of the evil snake.

Once, there were many crows living on a banyan tree. Near the tree, there was a cave in which a family of owls lived. The crows and the owls were enemies.

At night, the crows could not see as well as the owls could. So during the night, the owls would fly to the banyan tree and kill many crows.

The king crow called a meeting to discuss what could be done about the owls. There was a lot of discussion and finally, they arrived at a plan.

An old crow said, "Tomorrow, you all will beat me near the cave of the owls."

"What are you saying? How can we beat you for we respect you a lot," asked the surprised king crow.

"This would just be an eyewash, My Lord. After that I will do the rest. And yes, I want some blood. Please give it to me tomorrow," said the old crow.

The next day, around eight crows pretended to beat the old crow.

Then they quickly smeared some blood over the old crow and went away leaving the old crow behind. The old crow acted as if it was very hurt and cried, "Caeeeeiiw Caaeeeiiiooo."

As the crow had been beaten near the cave of the owls, one owl had witnessed the beating. He went to the king owl and narrated the incidence that had happened outside their cave.

The king owl told the owl to bring the old crow inside. The owl flew out and carried the old crow to the king owl. The old crow seemed half dead and was given something to eat.

Then the old crow told the king owl that he had been beaten because he had spoken in favour of the owls at the meeting of the crows.

The king owl said, "How nice of you! Please stay here and we will look after you. Get well soon and then we will fight with the crows who have beaten you."

Next morning, the old crow got up while the owls were still sleeping.

The crow knew that the owls could not see during the day, so he gathered many twigs from trees nearby. At the mouth of the cave where the owls lived, the crow piled the twigs and then set them on fire. The whole owl kingdom was burnt down and all the owls perished in the fire.

The old crow then flew back to the banyan tree. Everyone welcomed the wise old crow, and thanked him for getting them rid of the evil owls once and for all.

THE WOODCUTTER AND THE LION

A woodcutter went with his wife to a forest every day. The wife would cook food which they would carry with them.

One day, a lion was roaming in the forest, looking for something to eat. His friends, the jackal and the crow, who stayed with him all the time were not there.

All of a sudden, the lion saw the woodcutter, who also saw him at the same time. The wife climbed up a tree out of fear.

The scared woodcutter gathered his wits and said, "Come, dear lion. Come and eat the delicious food prepared by my wife."

The lion growled, "I eat only flesh, but since you insist, I will taste your food."

The woodcutter gave his entire food to the hungry lion, who relished every bite of it.

The pleased lion said, "Thank you so much. Don't worry, as you have been good to me, I will see that no animal troubles you when you are in the forest."

The woodcutter then said, "Please come and eat with us every day, but just come alone. I don't trust other animals."

The lion came daily and shared their food. He stopped hunting for he relished the food made by the woodcutter's wife.

The lion had stopped hunting, so his friends, the jackal and the crow went hungry.

This was because these two never hunted themselves but always ate the leftovers of the lion's hunt.

The jackal asked the lion one day, "Where do you go every day and why do you come back so happy?"

The lion kept quiet. But when they insisted, he told them about the woodcutter and his wife, and the mouth watering food they give him daily.

The jackal said, "Let us kill and eat them both."

The lion said, "No, they are my friends and nobody dare hurt them."

"If they are so nice, why don't you take us along with you?" asked the crow.

"All right, both of you can come and taste their food," replied the lion.

The woodcutter saw them coming towards him. He and his wife quickly climbed up the tree.

The lion saw them sitting on the tree and he asked, "I am your friend, then why have you both climbed the tree?"

The woodcutter replied, "I do not like your friends. You should keep good company, then we will be friends again."

The lion ordered the jackal and the crow to leave immediately. After this the woodcutter and the lion remained friends forever and enjoyed their meals together.

137

THE THANKLESS GOLDSMITH

A husband and a wife were so poor that they could not even feed their children. So the wife told the man to go and earn some money to buy food.

The man went out looking for a job. He lost his way and reached a forest. He was thirsty and looked around for water. Suddenly, he saw a well.

When he looked down the well, he saw a tiger, a monkey, a snake and a man inside the well.

The tiger said, "Please help me out. I promise not to harm you."

So the man helped him to come out of the well. Then he helped the monkey and the snake out of the well.

The three animals said, "Do come to our house so that we can repay you."

When the man in the well asked for help, all the animals said, "Don't take him out. Don't trust him. He is a man. Beware." But the poor man was kind and he helped the man in the well too to come out.

138

The man came out and said, "I am a goldsmith. If you ever need my help, feel free to come to me."

The poor man went to other cities but got no job and no money. Sad and upset, he went back to the well and met the three animals.

The tiger gave him a necklace of gold and said, "This necklace belongs to a prince whom I killed. It will help you."

The man remembered helping the goldsmith too. He wanted to sell the gold necklace for money, so he went to meet the goldsmith. When he showed the necklace, the goldsmith realised that it was the necklace he had made for the prince who had died in the forest.

The goldsmith told the man to wait and went to the king. He told the king about the man with the gold necklace. The king thought that the man had killed his son, so he had him chained and put him in the prison.

While in prison, the man was surprised to see the snake who had come to help him.

They hatched a plan. The snake gave a piece of a herb to the poor man, and then went and bit the queen.

Nobody could cure the queen who seemed to be dying. The man told the guards that he could cure any snake bite. The king was informed, who then ordered the man to be taken to the queen.

The man rubbed the herb on the bite mark, just as the snake had told him to. Soon the queen became well. The king ordered the soldiers to free the man and asked him about the necklace.

After listening to the whole story, the king punished the goldsmith and gave a lot of wealth and land to the poor man. The poor man became rich, and he and his family lived happily ever after.

141

THE MOSQUITO AND THE BUGS

A clever little bug and her whole family lived under the mattress of a king. They had been living there for a long time and were very happy.

She was clever enough to bite only when the king was sleeping soundly, was tired or drunk. She took care never to disturb the king's sleep.

So the king never came to know that the bug and her family were living in his bed. They were well fed and content.

But then one day, a mosquito sat on the king's bed. Incidentally, the king was not there, and the bug came out as the mosquito sat on the king's bed.

The bug felt angry and said, "Why have you come here? This is our house. You make such a buzzing noise that you will get all of us killed."

The mosquito replied, "This is the king's bed and it belongs to one and all. Moreover, I am your guest. It is your duty to look after me," further irritating the bug.

After a lot of begging, the bug allowed the mosquito to stay on the wooden bed post. She warned him not to buzz when the king was half asleep or awake.

After a while, the king came into the room and went to his bed.

The bugs quickly hid under the mattress.

Panchatantra

The bug wished that the mosquito would not bite the king then, but wait till he had slept soundly.

But the mosquito was hungry and could not wait. He bit the king on his hand.

The king screamed, "Soldiers! Something has bitten me. Turn the bed and check. I don't want to be bitten again."

As the king got up, the mosquito hid itself in the bedpost. But when the soldiers removed the sheets and turned the mattress, the whole family of bugs was shaken off the bed.

The poor bug got her whole family together with great difficulty and went and hid in a corner of the room.

The selfish mosquito was too happy to see them gone and started buzzing. One of the king's soldier saw it and squashed him between his palms.

That was the very end of the mosquito. The bug and her family then went and hid under the mattress as before. They were happy to get rid of the selfish mosquito forever.

THE MICE THAT ATE IRON

A merchant named Narud lost all his money in business. Left with no other choice, he pawned his iron balance with Lakshman, a pawn merchant.

Narud then left for another city to start a new business with that money. Narud was successful and upon returning to his city, he went to Lakshman to take his balance back. The merchant curtly told him that it had been eaten by mice.

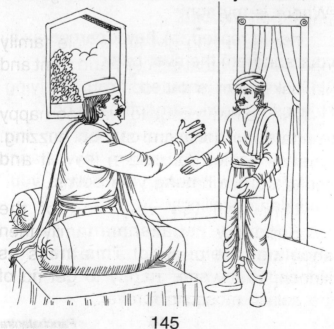

Narud was surprised that how would mice eat up an iron balance, but he did not argue.

He said, "You are not to be blamed Lakshman. These things happen. I am going for a bath to the river. Please send your son with me to carry my belongings."

The boy went with Narud to the river bank. After taking the bath, Narud took the boy home to his wife and asked her to take care of him. Narud then went back to Lakshman's house, who asked him, "Where is my son?"

Narud replied, "A hawk carried away your son from the river bank."

Lakshman shouted, "You are lying. How can a hawk carry off a big boy?"

"Just as the mice can eat my iron balance scale. You return my balance scale and I will bring your son to you," said Narud smilingly.

Suddenly, Lakshman started shouting, "Help! Help! This man has kidnapped my son."

The soldiers came and caught Narud, but he insisted that a hawk had carried off Lakshman's son.

The soldiers took both Narud and Lakshman to the king.

Lakshman complained to the king. "This man is lying that a hawk has carried off my son."

The surprised king asked, "How can a hawk carry off a fifteen year old boy?"

Then Narud spoke up, "Just as mice can eat a heavy iron balance scale, My Lord."

"What! How can mice eat iron things?" asked the king.

Then Narud narrated the whole story.

The king laughed and said, "Narud, that is a clever way to get your balance scale back. But why make his son suffer?"

Narud replied, "My lord, Lakshman's son is safe. He is with my wife at my house. She is taking good care of him.

The king then said, "Lakshman, give the balance scale back to Narud at once and then only, will he return your son."

Lakshman nodded his head.

The king continued, "But you, Lakshman, have done something very wrong. You will have to pay a fine for being so greedy and dishonest. Now give the balance scale back to him quickly."

WILL MONEY HELP?

A farmer had a small family. He owned a small piece of land which produced enough to feed his family. But he was greedy for more and more money.

He prayed to God to make him rich.

Pleased with his prayers, God appeared before him and asked, "What do you want?"

The man replied, "I want money."

God asked, "But what do you need money for? You and your family never go hungry. Then why this greed? You have only one mouth. How much can you eat?"

"I just want more money even if I don't need it," replied the greedy man.

God said, "Go to the city and visit two traders living there. One is called *Secret Wealth* and the other is called *Useful Wealth*."

The man first went to the house of *Secret Wealth* in the city. The family living there did not talk politely. The lady of the house gave a little food to him in a broken plate. When he asked for another serving, she rudely refused. He also heard other members speaking unpleasant words.

The man ate, and quietly left the house of *Secret Wealth*.

Then he went to the house of *Useful Wealth*. Here the family was not very rich but kind and polite. It surprisingly appeared to be happy and content. They served him wonderful food and made him feel very comfortable.

Suddenly, God appeared before him and the man said, "The *Secret Wealth* are rich people, but rude and unhappy with life. The *Useful Wealth* people are not so rich, yet are happy. I realise that it is not money itself but the way in which it is spent, which gives happiness, and nothing equals the joy of giving. From today, I will cherish whatever I have and not greed for more."

A milkman milked his cow and put the milk in an earthen pot to sell.

He got good money by selling the milk and bought more cows. Then the cows gave more milk which earned him a lot of money. He also prepared butter and curd from the milk.

He became rich by selling the butter and the curd in the market.

He married a beautiful girl and was very happy with her. She cooked good food and looked after the house very well.

Soon, his wife gave birth to a beautiful baby boy. As he grew, he played all over the house making a lot of noise.

One day, he became angry with his son and told him to stay quiet. But he would not listen and kept on shouting.

So the milkman picked up a stick and ran after his naughty son. The milkman tripped on something and his leg went up and hit something.

And look! what happened.

There was milk all over his body. He had kicked the pot of milk tied above his cot and the milk had spilled over him. He got up with surprise.

The milkman was alone on his bed. He had gone to sleep and had been daydreaming. There was no wife, no naughty son, no cows, nothing. There was no milk to sell which could have got him all that he saw in his dream.

The king rabbit had been very worried for the last few days. The rabbit family had always lived near a lake which had plenty of water. Now there was a problem.

Many elephants had come to stay near the lake as the other lakes had dried up because there had been no rains.

The elephants did not trouble the rabbits deliberately, but when they walked, their huge feet would often hurt the rabbits.

Tiny as they were, they would get hurt and some would even get killed beneath the elephants' huge feet.

The king rabbit decided that he should do something for his rabbit family. He thought deeply and then made a plan.

The king rabbit sat on a high rock on the way to the lake. As the king elephant was passing by, the rabbit shouted, "Wait, King Elephant, please wait."

The elephant stopped on hearing the voice of the rabbit.

The rabbit spoke in a very loud voice, "I live with the Moon God and am the king of the rabbits. You have been crushing many of us under your huge feet when you go towards the lake to drink water."

The elephant was scared thinking that the king rabbit must be very strong.

The rabbit went on, "The Moon God has also seen you all and is very angry with all of you for hurting the rabbits."

The king elephant said, "But we also want water from this lake."

"No, you should go away if you are harming someone," shouted the rabbit.

Then the king elephant said, "I don't want to harm anyone. I want to apologise to the Moon God. So, please take me there at once."

The clever king rabbit asked the king elephant to come to the lake on a full moon night.

On the full moon night, the king rabbit and the king elephant stood near the lake. The rabbit asked the elephant to look into the water of the lake. The king elephant saw the round reflection of the moon in the water.

A breeze blew and the water moved. The moon in the water became wavy and the rabbit said, "See, how angry the Moon God is. He might punish you all, if you don't apologise."

"But why is the Moon God favouring the rabbits?" asked the elephant.

The rabbit replied, "The rabbits have always lived here. Now look at the moon and then look at me; we are of the same colour. We both are milky white and so are very special to the Moon God. So the Moon God cares for us a lot."

The king elephant was really frightened because he thought that the Moon God would be very angry with the elephants for hurting his favourite rabbits.

So, the king elephant apologised, "Oh! Moon God, I am really sorry. Please forgive all of us. We will not trouble the rabbits any more. We will leave this place at once and go to some other lake. Kindly accept my apologies."

The next morning, the king elephant called all the other elephants, and ordered them to march away from that place.

The elephants started walking away from the lake, with their children in the centre and the older elephants around them.

The rabbits saw them going and then the king rabbit said, "The elephants are actually very caring. See how nicely they look after their children."

The queen rabbit added, "But they are too big and heavy. I am happy that they are leaving this place."

All the rabbits rejoiced and were happy that the elephants were going away and would no longer hurt them. The rabbits danced and sang and made merry. They lived happily ever after near the lake.

Once a holy man lived in a deep, dark forest. He prayed and meditated a lot.

Many people would come to the forest and he would advise them on ways to deal with their problems. The pleased villagers presented him with lot of money. The holy man became worried that someone might steal his money. He kept the money in a cloth bag and carried it under his arm all the time.

Once a thief happened to pass by and saw the people offering money and gifts to the holy man. The thief hatched a plan to loot his money.

He went to the holy man and said, "I respect you immensely and want to be your loyal follower."

The holy man was very happy that someone would be staying with him. So he readily agreed. All this while, the thief was eyeing the money and the gifts.

One day, taking advantage of the holy man's absence, the thief thoroughly searched his house, but failed to find any money.

The next day, the thief followed the holy man to the river. The holy man took off his clothes and stepped into the river. The moment he did this, the thief picked up his clothes and ran away. The holy man tried to chase him, but the thief was young and strong so he got away.

The holy man was very sad and upset to lose all his money. But then he realised that his greed for money had taken him away from God.

He wondered "When the money was with me, I always remained worried. But now that the money has been stolen, I have nothing to worry about."

He realised that money had made him suffer. He now knew that it was better to stay without too much money, and be happy and peaceful. Now the holy man, began spending his time in praying to God again and donating the gifts and money he got, to the needy. He found more happiness in that.